Bible

New Testament
Activities for Kids

Warner
Press Kids
educate • nurture • inspire
www.warnerpress.org

Copyright ©2006 Warner Press, Inc
All rights reserved
Printed in USA
305800214852

Jesus as a Child

Use the key below to decode a Bible verse that describes Jesus as a young child.

A=1 B=2 C=3 D=4 E=5 F=6 G=7 H=8 I=9 J=10 K=11
L=12 M=13 N=14 O=15 P=16 Q=17 R=18 S=19 T=20 U=21
V=22 W=23 X=24 Y=25 Z=26

__ __ __   __ __ __ __ __   __ __ __ __   __ __ __   __ __ __ __ __
20 8 5   3 8 9 12 4   7 18 5 23   1 14 4   2 5 3 1 13 5

__ __ __ __ __ __; __ __   __ __ __   __ __ __ __ __ __   __ __ __ __
19 20 18 15 14 7   8 5   23 1 19   6 9 12 12 5 4   23 9 20 8

__ __ __ __ __ __, __ __ __   __ __ __   __ __ __ __ __   __ __   __ __ __
23 9 19 4 15 13   1 14 4   20 8 5   7 18 1 3 5   15 6   7 15 4

__ __ __   __ __ __ __   __ __ __.   Luke 2:40
23 1 19   21 16 15 14   8 9 13

In His Steps

Starting at the fishing boat, follow the path to find what the fishermen did when they left their nets.

Let's Pray

Use words in the word box to complete the sentences. Then copy those words on the puzzle at the bottom of the page. The circled letters will spell something that was important to Jesus. It is also something that needs to be important in your life.

Word Box

helps	everything	pray
friends	talking	Father

1. God ___ ___ ___ ___ ___ us when we pray.

2. Jesus prayed, "___ ___ ___ ___ ___ ___, I want to do your will."

3. Prayer is ___ ___ ___ ___ ___ ___ ___ with God.

4. Lord, teach us to ___ ___ ___ ___. (Luke 11:1)

5. Jesus told his ___ ___ ___ ___ ___ ___ ___ to pray.

6. God is interested in ___ ___ ___ ___ ___ ___ ___ ___ ___ ___ that happens to us.

The Lord's Prayer

Read the Lord's Prayer in your Bible: Matthew 6:9-13. Then complete the phrases in the Lord's Prayer by filling in the blanks on the crossword puzzle.

1. Forgive us our _____.

2. Our _____ in heaven

3. On earth as it is in _____

4. Lead us not into _____

5. Give us _____ our daily bread

6. Deliver us from the evil _____

7. Hallowed be your _____

8. Your will be _____

Jesus Heals a Paralyzed Man

One day some men brought their friend who was paralyzed to Jesus. Jesus told the man, "Your sins are forgiven." Some teachers of the law didn't like what Jesus said, so instead Jesus said, "Get up, take your mat and walk." Why did Jesus heal the man?

Use the code to find the letters that fit in the blank. Match the arrangement of the lines with those in the code. The first one is done for you.

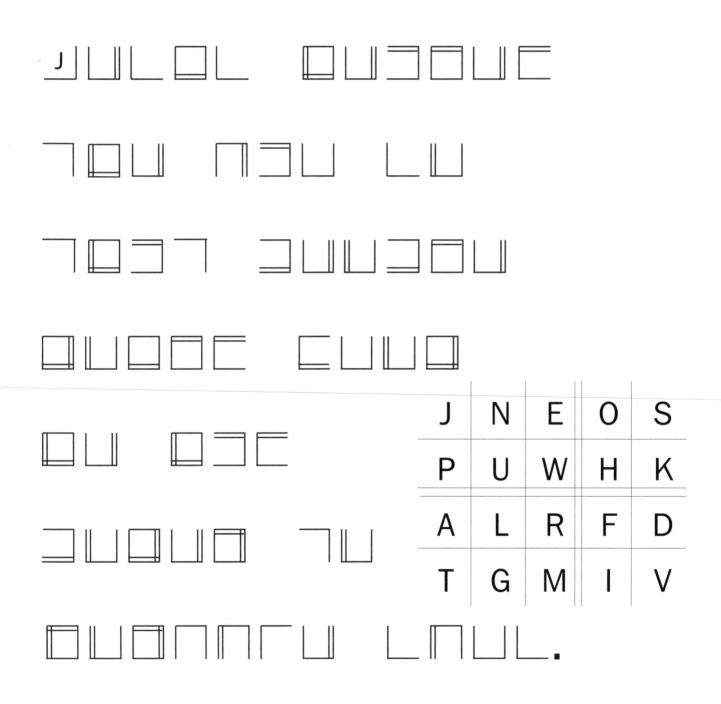

J	N	E	O	S
P	U	W	H	K
A	L	R	F	D
T	G	M	I	V

Jesus and the Rich Young Man

One day a rich young man asked Jesus what he should do to receive eternal life. Write down the first letter from the Letter List in the first blank. Then skip the second letter and place the third letter in the next blank. Continue by placing every other letter in the blanks. Then read what Jesus said.

Letter List

JTELSUUISCLNOMODKWEPDIABTGHQIZMEAINLDPLIOCVYEJDSHXIEMPOEN

WEDTJHSILNKGOYDOCUWLSAKCEKSHRECSIAMIWDVGEOXSKEFLQLKEMVI

EORSYCTKHOISNXGCYWOVUJHOAMVIEOAPNWDAGSIDVFEGTHOJTKH

LEZPXOCOVRBAMNQDWYEORUTWYIULILOHPASVDEFTGRHEJAKSLUZRXECI

VNBHNEMAQVWERNYTUHIEONPCAOSMDEGFHOJLKLZOXWCMVE.

_ _ _ _ _   _ _ _ _ _ _   _ _   _ _   _ _ _   _ _ _ _ _

_ _ _.   " _ _ _   _ _ _ _ _   _ _ _   _ _ _ _,"   _ _

_ _ _ _.   " _ _,   _ _ _ _   _ _ _ _ _ _ _ _ _   _ _ _

_ _ _ _ _   _ _ _   _ _ _ _ _   _ _   _ _ _   _ _ _ _,   _ _ _

_ _   _ _ _ _   _ _ _   _ _ _ _ _ _

_ _   _ _ _ _ _.   _ _ _ _ _   _ _ _ _ _,   _ _ _ _ _ _   _ _."

Mark 10:21

Blind Bartimaeus

Read the story of Blind Bartimaeus in your Bible: Mark 10:46-52. Then find and circle these words from the story. Words will be found going up, down, across or backwards.

Faith
Prayer
Follow
Healed
Blind
Go

Jesus
Shout
Bartimaeus
Beggar
Mercy
Calling

```
K  X  A  M  E  R  C  Y  W  F  M  J  P  F  J
U  H  T  I  A  F  A  R  P  B  A  Y  B  O  C
R  L  G  W  J  T  L  L  R  E  J  Q  L  D  I
S  D  U  O  U  F  L  E  A  Q  B  O  I  Q  R
I  C  V  L  L  K  I  T  Y  M  P  X  N  A  S
R  I  V  L  V  K  N  H  E  A  L  E  D  C  I
J  C  G  O  W  B  G  P  R  Z  O  L  Z  E  G
E  N  I  F  M  S  T  Q  Y  D  N  R  A  F  M
S  H  U  T  J  H  M  C  S  B  E  G  G  A  R
U  K  B  A  H  O  B  S  O  P  U  W  E  G  R
S  L  A  L  B  U  C  P  Z  O  Y  E  A  Q  S
I  X  B  A  R  T  I  M  A  E  U  S  S  W  F
N  O  T  G  R  T  N  Z  A  N  D  W  H  E  H
A  L  Y  T  C  P  G  K  F  X  G  V  C  H  A
```

Message at the Well

The first part of some Bible verses is written at the top of the water jar. Write these words on the blanks inside the jar: *Then, leaving her water jar, the woman went back to the town and said to the people,*

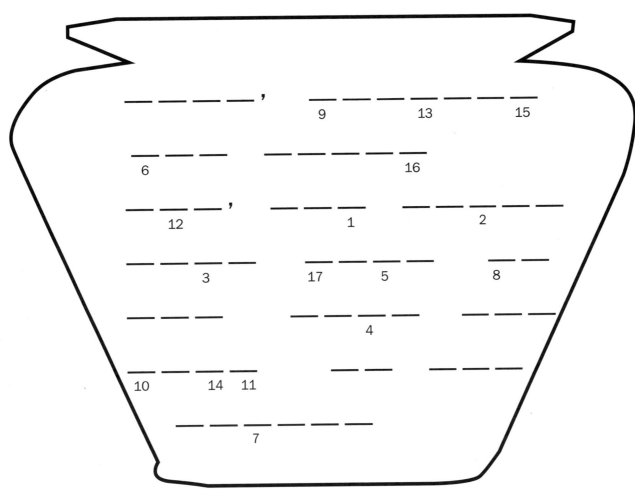

Now use the numbered letters in the jar above to fill in the blanks in the code below.

"
___ ___ ___ ___ , ___ ___ ___ ___ ___ ___ ___ ___ ___ ___
5   7   2   1   10 1   1   12   2 12   3   4   6   7

___ ___ ___ ___ ___ ___ ___ ___ ___ Y ___ ___ ___ ___ ___ ___
8   7   9   11   2   1   1   13 1 16   8   6 14   3 15 14

___ ___ ___ ___ ___ ___ ___ . ___ ___ U ___ ___ ___ ___ ___ ___
1   13 1   16   11 14 11   5   7   9 11   8   6 14 10

___ ___ ___ ___ ___ ___ ___ ___ ___ ___ ___ ?" John 4:28–29
17 1   8   6   1   5   6 16 14 10   8

Jesus Heals a Blind Man

Jesus healed people wherever He went. Once He healed a man who was born blind. Jesus asked the man if he believed in Him. What was the man's response?

Braille is a special system of raised dots that helps people who cannot see to read. Can you write the Bible verse below using braille?

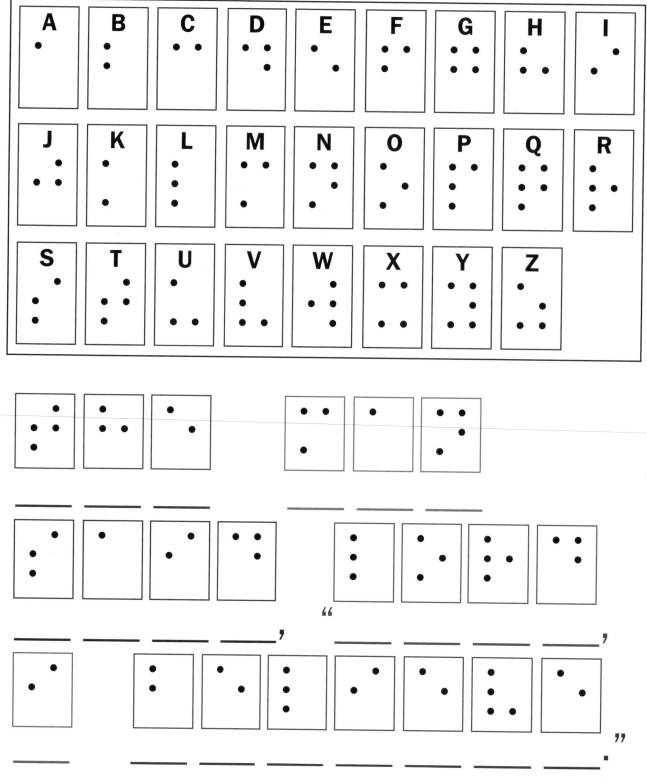

John 9:38

Why Jesus Prayed

Use a ruler to draw a line from the problem dot to the answer dot. The line will go through a circled letter. Write the letter in the blank next to the answer. You will spell a message that tells why Jesus prayed in a lonely place.

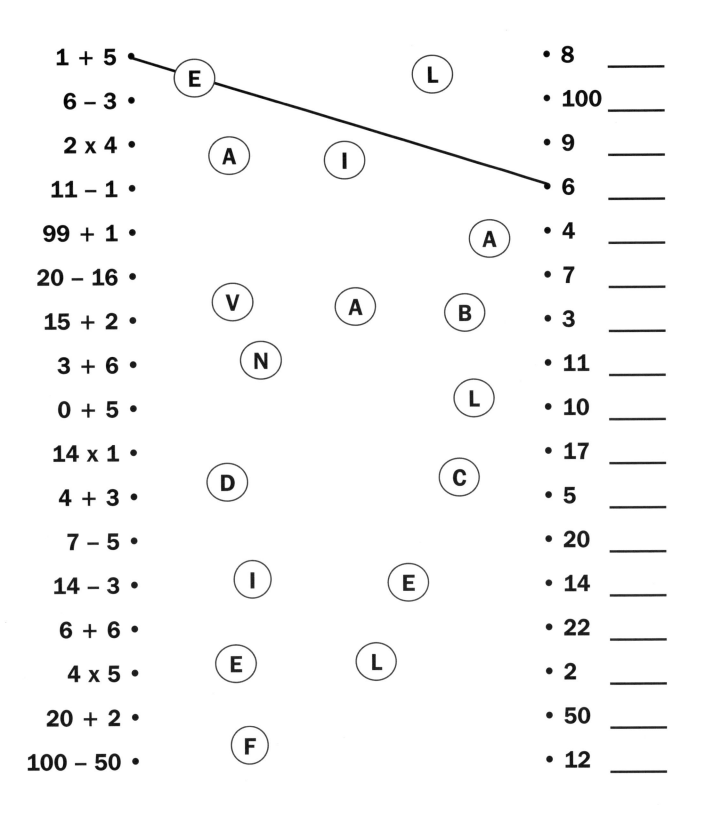

1 + 5

6 – 3

2 x 4

11 – 1

99 + 1

20 – 16

15 + 2

3 + 6

0 + 5

14 x 1

4 + 3

7 – 5

14 – 3

6 + 6

4 x 5

20 + 2

100 – 50

8 ____
100 ____
9 ____
6 ____
4 ____
7 ____
3 ____
11 ____
10 ____
17 ____
5 ____
20 ____
14 ____
22 ____
2 ____
50 ____
12 ____

E L A I A V A B N L D C I E E L F

Jesus Appears to His Disciples

Do the math problems. Then match the answers with the alphabet code. You will find out the names of some of the disciples who were fishing the morning Jesus cooked breakfast on the beach.

a	b	d	e	h	i	j	l	m	n	o	p	r	s	t	u	y	z
1	2	3	4	5	6	7	8	9	10	11	12	13	14	15	16	17	18

```
  6      4      8      3      9           20     12     15     11     34     16
 +6     +0     +7     +1     +4           -5     -7     - 4    -2     -33    -2
 [12]   [ ]    [ ]    [ ]    [ ]          [ ]    [ ]    [ ]    [ ]    [ ]    [ ]

  P     ___    ___    ___    ___          ___    ___    ___    ___    ___    ___
```

```
  5      1      6      9      7     13     16      8      2
 +5     +0     +9     -4     -6     -3     -15     -4     +6
 [ ]    [ ]    [ ]    [ ]    [ ]    [ ]    [ ]     [ ]    [ ]

 ___    ___    ___    ___    ___    ___    ___     ___    ___
```

```
  5      9      6      7      7            3      14      2      4
 +2     -8     +3     -3     +7           +4     -3     +3     +6
 [ ]    [ ]    [ ]    [ ]    [ ]          [ ]    [ ]    [ ]    [ ]

 ___    ___    ___    ___    ___          ___    ___    ___    ___
```

How many other disciples were there? 7–5=_____ others.

Look in John 21:2 and Matthew 4:21 to check your answers.

The Path to Peace

Start with anger in the maze below and find your way to peace. If you follow the attitudes described in Galatians 5:22–23, you will reach the finish.

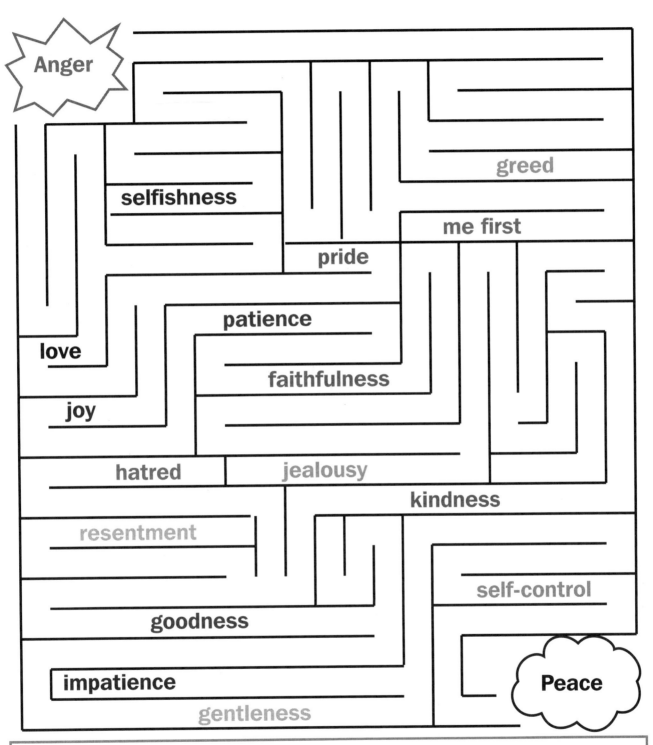

Anger

greed

selfishness

me first

pride

patience

love

faithfulness

joy

hatred   jealousy

kindness

resentment

self-control

goodness

impatience   Peace

gentleness

But the fruit of the Spirit is love, joy, peace, patience, kindness, goodness, faithfulness, gentleness and self-control. Against such things there is no law.
Galatians 5:22–23

Living for God

1. desk	God's	chair
2. chosen	dog	cat
3. blue	red	people
4. crayon	pencil	holy
5. loved	truck	car
6. milk	clothe	water
7. compassion	sock	shoe
8. little	big	kindness

9. humility	ball	toy
10. hand	foot	gentleness
11. hat	patience	coat
12. apple	orange	Bear
13. forgive	sun	moon
14. tree	grievances	flower
15. against	yellow	pink
16. two	five	another

In each group of three words, two belong together. Cross out the words that belong together. Print the words that are left in order on the lines below.

Therefore, as _____ _____ _____,

_____ and dearly _____, _____ yourselves with

_____, _____,

_____, _____, and

_____. _____ with each other and

_____ whatever _____ you may have

_____ one _____.

Colossians 3:12–13

Good Words to Follow

Follow the maze to find words from a Bible verse in 1 Thessalonians.
As you find the letters, write them in the blanks.

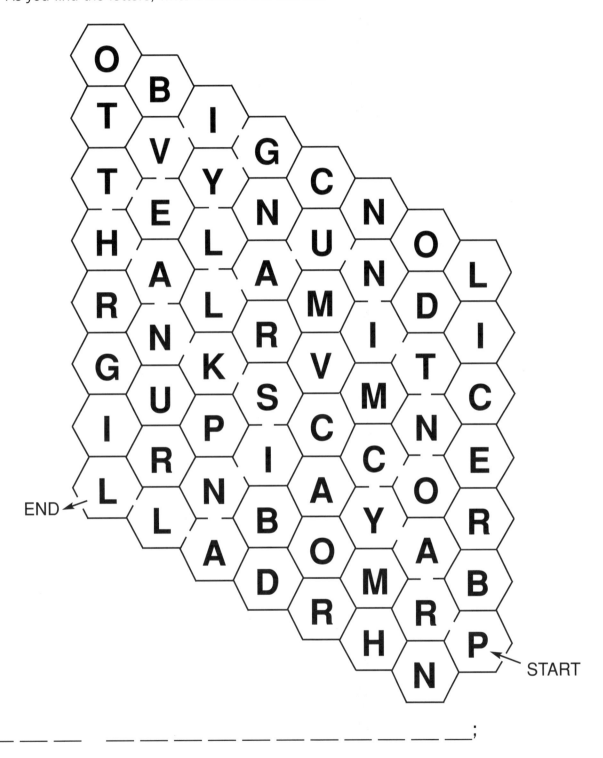

____ _____ _____ _____ ;

____ _____

circumstances, for this is God's will for you in Christ Jesus.

1 Thessalonians 5:17–18

What Is Faith?

The Apostle Paul wrote many letters to encourage believers in Jesus. Read Hebrews 11 in your Bible to see how Paul explained the meaning of faith.

See if you can figure out this message written in sign language. Then try to form the code with your own hands. Did it seem as if it took forever to spell out this short message? It's not easy! We should admire people who have to use this language all the time and have compassion for them.

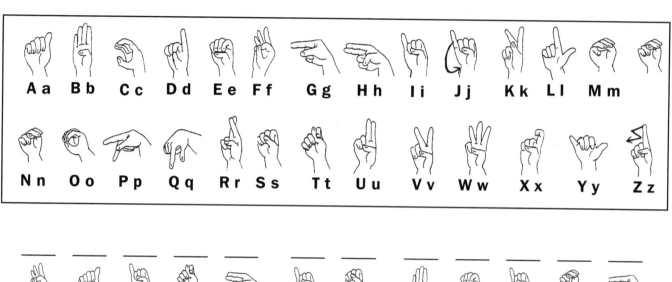

A a   B b   C c   D d   E e   F f   G g   H h   I i   J j   K k   L l   M m

N n   O o   P p   Q q   R r   S s   T t   U u   V v   W w   X x   Y y   Z z

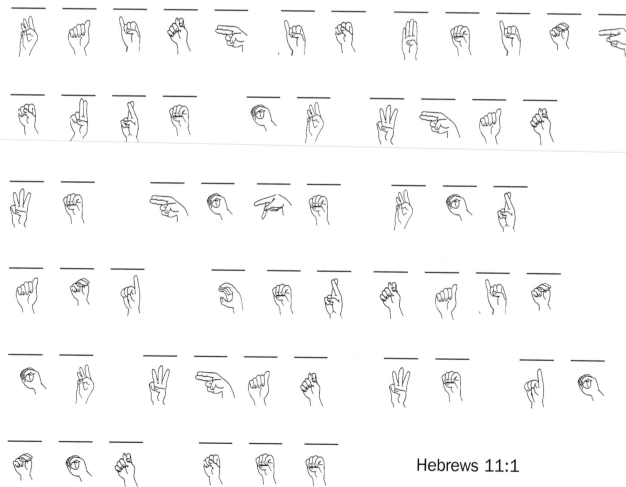

Hebrews 11:1